C000007644

BUSES
& TAXIS

This book belongs to:

James Parker

DOUBLE-DECKER BUSES

Double-deck buses have always been popular in Britain. Horse-drawn vehicles established the layout in the nineteenth century. Early motor buses followed that basic design. During the 1920s, the top decks were roofed over, and the stairs were fully enclosed by the early 1930s. The double-deck bus then remained largely unchanged until the late 1950s. It had vertical front engine, half-cab for the driver, and an open rear entrance with a conductor to take the fares.

With the coming of reliable remote-control systems during the 1960s, the front-entrance, rear-engined types became more widespread and a one-person operation became possible. Where traffic was particularly dense, notably in Central London, the classic front-engined, open rear entrance bus, fought a valiant rear-guard action. Here the famous London Routemaster is still King.

Horse-drawn Bus
Stanilas Baudry of Nantes in France started the first short-stage coach outside a shop belonging to a M. Omnes and gave the service the name 'Omnes Omnibus'. George Shillibeer introduced the idea to Britain in 1829. Horse-drawn buses can still be seen in tourist areas, and at carnivals and rallies.
I-Spy for 25

Early Motor Bus
The London General Omnibus Company had its buses made for it by AEC. This 'K' type still looks like a horse-drawn vehicle and runs on solid tyres.
I-Spy for 25

AEC R.T.

Probably the most famous bus ever made, this is the definitive 'London Bus'. It represented a significant advance in bus design with air-operated brakes and gearbox. Introduced in 1940, they remained in service until April 1979. Many survive in preservation and on vintage services.
I-Spy for 15

AEC Routemaster

Conventional in appearance, this bus is technically advanced. It was designed to replace trolley buses and entered service in 1959. Manufacture ceased in 1968 after 2760 had been built. The monocoque body incorporates aircraft technology, and the brakes are pressure hydraulic. Independent coil-spring suspension and epicyclic automatic gearbox are key features. It is still on active service in London. What do the letters 'AEC' stand for?
I-Spy for 10 — double with answer _____

3

AEC Routemaster (Long)

London Transport Designation 'RML'. Park Royal Bodies extended the 27-foot (8.2-m) long: 64-seat Routemaster to 30 feet (9.1 m) and 72 seats simply by adding a short, 2 foot 4 inch (71-cm) bay to the centre of the vehicle. Look out for the additional square window amidships and longer-than-average wheel base. The final 500 (1965-68) were built to this specification.
*I-Spy for **10***

AEC Routemaster

The open rear-entrance bus with conductor on board enjoyed a revival in the mid 1980s and second-hand ex-London Routemasters have appeared throughout Britain.
*I-Spy for **20***

AEC Regent

This was the mainstream double-deck chassis from this once-famous Southall (London) manufacturer. Regents were made from 1929 until 1968 — initially with petrol engines, then diesel. Exposed radiators were replaced with a tin front from 1956. Many are preserved or kept as 'learner buses' for training drivers in the art of manual gear changing for full PCV driving licences.
What do the letters 'PCV' stand for? _____

Lowbridge

This example is 27 feet (8.2 m) long. It displays an exposed radiator and is fitted with 56-seat, low-height, MCW bodywork.
I-Spy for 25

Highbridge

Later Regents are 30 feet (9.1 m) long and have 'tin fronts'. This example is the 'high bridge' type with a Park Royal body.
I-Spy for 20

Bristol Lowdekka
The Bristol Lowdekka with its Eastern Coachworks body was, for many years, the standard double-deck bus outside London. Virtually indestructible, these buses have found ready buyers second- and even tenth-hand! Powered by a 5- or 6-cylinder Gardner diesel engine, they are used as school and workmen's special buses. 'Top Deck Holidays' have a fleet of fifty used on continental self-catering tours.
I-Spy for 20

Bristol V.R.
Successor to the Lowdekka, the V.R. was Bristol's version of the rear-engined type. It was usually bodied in Lowestoft by Eastern Coachworks and powered by Gardner. Look out for bodies with front entry and centre exit doors to speed loading and unloading during peak hours city use.
I-Spy for 5
Double for a V.R. with bodywork other than ECW!

Daimler Fleetline

Once builders of high-quality cars, Daimler was also a long-established bus- and coachmaker. The traditional fluted top on early Daimler radiators was made a feature of the maker's badge. The Fleetline was mechanically similar to Atlantean, but with a drop centre rear axle.
I-Spy for 15

Daimler DMS

The DMS has had a chequered history. It was introduced in 1970 for London Transport as a Routemaster replacement; service difficulties resulted in premature sale in 1979. Eager buyers as far away as Hong Kong have put them to good use.
I-Spy for 10

Dennis

Dennis Vehicles at Guildford is an old, established company that has survived by tailoring its product to the customers' needs. The company also made fire appliances, dust carts, and specialist vehicles. Old Dennises are survivors and many exist in preservation.
I-Spy for 25

Dennis Dominator

The Dennis Dominator was developed in conjunction with Leicester City Transport. Many operators see it as the successor to the Daimler Fleetline.
I-Spy for 10

Leyland PD2

This is Leyland's traditional front vertical-engined, drop-frame chassis. Originally it had an exposed radiator, and was then modernized with a tin front. It is rare now and seen only at rallies and in museums.

I-Spy 25 each for exposed radiator and tin front

Leyland Atlantean

This was the first successful application of the vertical transverse rear-engine layout. The prominent bustle or bonnet at the rear is a good recognition point. Fifteen thousand were built and many, like this 'open topper', still give good service.

I-Spy for 10

Leyland Titan

This was a sophisticated integral double decker designed for London. At first, it was built by Park Royal. Production transferred to Workington, but ceased in 1984. Second-hand examples are found throughout Britain.
I-Spy for **15**

Leyland Olympian

The Olympian was introduced in 1980 as a one-model replacement for the Atlantean, VR, and Fleetline ranges. Engine options are Leyland TL11 or Gardner 6LXB. New in 1987, this one has Alexander bodywork.
I-Spy for **5**

MCW Metropolitan
The MCW Metropolitan was the result of co-operation between one of Britain's oldest and most respected coachbuilders, Metro Cammel Weyman, and Scania of Sweden. The latter supplying runner gear and power units to the Birmingham builder.
I-Spy for 15

Metrobus Integral
Natural successor to the Metropolitan, the Metrobus Integral is an all-British product using Gardner power, Voith automatic transmission, and air suspension. Early versions have cab windows of unequal depth. Mk IIs have a simpler, more conventional front end.
I-Spy 10 for each

Metroliner

Metroliner was MCW's answer to continental double-deck coaches which were being imported in increasing numbers from 1982. The 12-metre (39-ft), three-axle vehicle is powered by a 290 HP L10 Cummins diesel driving through Voith transmission.

I-Spy for 15

Volvo Ailsa

Built in Scotland by this famous Swedish commercial manufacturer, the Ailsa front-engined double decker is particularly popular with Scottish and northern operators. The compact 6.7-litre, turbo-charged engine sits alongside the driver behind a large rectangular front grille.

I-Spy for 10

The single-deck bus or coach evolved from the *charabanc* or large motor car. Many early coaches comprised a crude body mounted on a World War 1 army surplus lorry. By the 1930s, purpose-built chassis were clothed in increasingly elegant and luxurious bodies.

In the mid-1950s, the major technical innovation was to lay the largest and most powerful engines on their sides amidships under the floor of the coach or bus. This allowed more room for passengers. During the 1980s, the decline of British Leyland created a vacuum in the supply of vehicles, and foreign manufacturers have taken an increasing share of chassis and body markets. To recognize the make of the chassis look out for front and rear badge motifs as well as the shape of the wheels, and the layout of controls.

AEC Regal
This was the single-deck equivalent of the Regent made from 1929 until 1957. The last four years' production went to export markets. It is now rare and confined to museums, rallies, and 'vintage' services.
I-Spy for 25

AEC Regal Mk IV
The Midland Red Omnibus Company was the first to lay an engine on its side under a chassis and make it work reliably. This was AEC's version, initially developed for London Transport as the R. F. series. Refined, developed, and lightened, it became the Reliance.
I-Spy for 20

AEC
The blue triangle badge is usually set in 'speed wings' and the front wheels have chromium nut rings fitted.
I-Spy for 10

AEC Reliance
The AEC Reliance was introduced in 1953 and was popular until 1980. Its engine size was increased from 7.7 to 9.6 litres and the length went up from 8.1 metres (27 ft) to 11 metres (36 ft). Like most AECs, this bus is very durable and many remain in service.
I-Spy for 10

Bedford
Bedford was the bus- and lorry-building subsidiary of Vauxhall Motors, a division of General Motors of America. The marque disappeared in 1988 because of falling sales and other reasons. The badge is a rampant Griffon with 'V' for Vauxhall flag! Where were Bedford coaches made?
I-Spy for 10 — double with answer _____

Bedford OB
This 29-seat coach, powered by a 6-cylinder, 3.5-litre petrol engine, re-established the coach industry after World War 2. Cheap, simple, and tough, many are still in active service and enjoying a second life. This example was providing a classic bus service at a wedding.
I-Spy for 20

Bedford SB

The Bedford SB was the logical development of the OB, introducing 'forward control' (where the driver sits alongside or above the engine) and diesel-engined options. This service bus version is seen ending its days as a mobile tattooing parlour!
I-Spy for 20

Bedford VAL

The Bedford VAL offered a unique solution to low floor height coaching by using six small wheels on a twin-steer chassis. Once their coaching days were over, they were eagerly sought out as racing car transporters. This example is now a luxury motor home using a modified Plaxton Panorama body.
I-Spy for 25

15

Bedford VAM
Conservative operators who favoured a four-wheeled chassis could order the VAM which followed the Bedford tradition of cheap, reliable, no-frills coaching. For this reason, many still exist, providing transport to bands, clubs, majorette troupes, and scouts. These scouts have the luxury of a Duple body.
I-Spy for 15

Bedford 'Midi'
Representing one of the last Bedford chassis to go into service, this 'midi'-sized coach with a Plaxton body is based on a shortened version of the 'Y'-type chassis.
I-Spy for 10

Bristol

Single-deck Bristols are becoming rare but the LH model, usually built to a narrow width of 2.28 metres (7½ ft) and shorter length of 8.765 metres (28¾ ft), is so rugged and useful that many operators are loath to part with them. They are usually found with bus rather than coach bodies.

I-Spy for 15

Bristol RE

This was a full-size, horizontal, rear-engined chassis for building up as a bus (this example) or coach. Bristols were made in the city of that name until 1983.

I-Spy for 15

DAF

DAF originated in Holland in 1949. The Van Doorne brothers started by renovating old army trucks with Leyland engines. The MB200 chassis is a popular import. This example has Van Hool coachwork.
I-Spy for **10**

Dennis Lancet

Smallest of the Dennis chassis, the Lancet makes a good 'midi' bus. The 'Handy Bus' body is a product of the Wright Company of Ballymena, Northern Ireland.
I-Spy for **10**

Dennis Javelin
The Dennis Javelin chassis features a vertical, rear-mounted Cummins L10 engine driving through a 6-speed ZF gearbox. This one carries a body made by Duple (one of the last produced by this famous coach-builder).
I-Spy for 10

Dennis Dorchester
The Dennis Dorchester is this company's premium-quality coach chassis introduced in 1982. It incorporates air suspension and is powered by horizontal Gardner or Rolls Royce engine options. This example carries Caetano coachwork.
I-Spy for 10

Ford 'R' Series
The other American-owned, British-based company, Ford, enjoyed buoyant sales throughout the 1970s and '80s. The heavy commercial division has been absorbed into the Iveco organization, leaving just the Transit-based minibus in production. Many R6 heavyweight coaches are still run by small operators.
I-Spy for 10

19

Kassbohrer-Setra

The Setra integral coach is produced in Germany by Kassbohrer and is highly regarded by the coaching industry and by other builders. The S215HD is powered by a rear-mounted Mercedes-Benz diesel. The ornate 'K' insignia features in the centre of the grille and wheel trims.

I-Spy for 15

Leyland Leopard

Another durable and long-lasting British chassis, the Leyland Leopard was in production from 1959 until 1981 when the Tiger came along. Recognition points are: large cast aluminium 'dinner plates' on the front wheels and a very deep, 'throaty' exhaust noise! This one has been given a new Duple body.

I-Spy for 5

Leyland Tiger

The Leyland Tiger replaced the Leopard and the AEC Reliance in 1981. At first it was available as a Maximum Permitted Length 12-metre (39-ft) chassis with a 218 BHP TL II mid-mounted engine. Later the engine was uprated to 260 BHP. This example carries a Plaxton body.

I-Spy for 5

Leyland

An easy recognition point for this Leyland product! What is the other manufacturer of PCVs based in Lancashire?

_____

_____

_____

I-Spy for 5
Double with answer

Leyland 'Royal Tiger Doyen'

This coach is Leyland's answer to the foreign integral coaches which have become popular in recent years. The Leyland engine is rear mounted in a body manufactured by Roe at Leeds. Massive underfloor luggage lockers are a feature of this design. The impressive grille badge is probably the most ornate ever to grace a motor vehicle.

I-Spy 15 for each

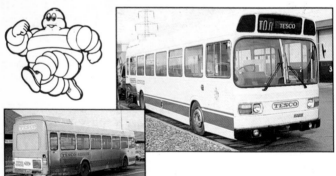

Leyland National Mk I

The Leyland National single-deck bus was a radical departure from convention. Of integral and modular design, it was made in a dedicated new factory at Workington, from 1970. The Mark I used a Leyland fixed-head 510 diesel engine, and can be identified by a flat, featureless front panel and a rear-mounted radiator with fan drive behind a coarse-mesh grille.

I-Spy for 5

Leyland National Mk II

The Mk II Leyland National incorporated many improvements which overcame faults experienced with the earlier model. It can be distinguished by a bulbous front with forward-mounted radiator. There is a total of 8000 out there to I-Spy!
I-Spy for 5

MAN

MAN has enjoyed some success exporting complete coaches to Britain. The distinctive SR 280 has been bought by several prominent operators and these coaches are sought-after second-hand buys. Watch for the dog insignia and a central 'snout' on the rectangular grille. MAN is a German company which pioneered the use of the diesel engine.
I-Spy for 15

Mercedes-Benz

Mercedes-Benz was the first continental manufacturer to target the British coach market in 1967 with the 0302 integral (chassis-less construction). More recent imports are chassis only for building up into the traditional British body-on-chassis coach. What is the Mercedes-Benz logo?

I-Spy for 15 — double with answer

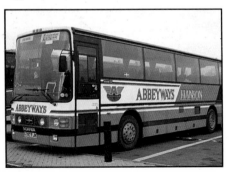

Scania

Scania's origins go back to 1891 and the Vabis Railway Carriage company. The first commercial vehicles came in 1903. Britain has taken significant imports from Sweden since 1972. Scania favours a rear-engined layout.

I-Spy for 10

Seddon Atkinson
Seddon Atkinson is Lancashire's other bus builder (Leyland is more famous). The RU and Pennine models, in varying lengths and powered by Perkins or Gardner, are most popular in Scotland and the north of England.
I-Spy for 15

Volvo
This Swedish manufacturer is a world leader in bus and truck manufacture. Number one importer, they bought out Leyland Bus in 1988. The popular Biom chassis is underfloor engined, as was its predecessor, the B58 model.
I-Spy for 5

MINIBUSES

During the 1970s and '80s, the numbers of bus passengers declined, city centres became more congested, and operating costs soared. During the 1980s, bus services were 'deregulated' and the industry came up with this new innovation — the minibus. Low start-up cost and the greater likelihood of operating with most of the seats filled made the idea attractive to operators.

Early minibuses were all too obviously based on small delivery vans. They were cramped and uncomfortable, and proved not to be robust enough in important features such as transmission and brakes. More recent vehicles are purpose designed for PCV use and sizes are creeping up towards the conventional single-decker.

Caetano
The Portuguese Caetano integral minibus offers great style and luxury in a small package. Power comes from a Japanese Toyota diesel.
I-Spy for 10

Ford Transit
Pioneers, and very successful in the minibus market, Ford Transit minibuses show their 'bread van' parentage: bodies by Dormobile, Hawson, and Carlyle are popular.
I-Spy for 5

Freight Rover

This minibus is an all-Freight Rover product fitted out to full PCV standard. It will be carrying a first aid kit and fire extinguisher. All doors and emergency exits will be prominently labelled, seating capacity and owner's name and address clearly marked. The gap between the body and the road will be minimized by fitting side panels or life rails.
I-Spy for 10

Iveco

Iveco is the European consortium formed from Fiat (Italy), Magirus Deutz (Germany), Unic (France), and Ford (Britain) — a big company for a little bus! This one has Plaxton coachwork.
I-Spy for 10

MAN-Volkswagen

MAN-Volkswagen entered the minibus market with adapted LT-type panel vans, and now offer chassis units for specialist coachwork — note the MAN dog motif.
I-Spy for 10

Mercedes

Mercedes were originally supplied as trimmed-out standard panel vans. The small Mercedes is favoured by Carlyle and Reeve Burgess as the basis of custom-built minibuses.
I-Spy for 5

Metro Rider

Metro Rider was MCW's entry in the minibus market. It uses a Cummins 6B diesel driving through an Alison autobox. Optare, the Leeds-based coachbuilder, now has manufacturing rights and has developed stretched versions.
I-Spy for 10

Minibus Sitting Case Ambulance

Operated by health authorities, these are often modified by fitting large tail doors and wheelchair lifts. Devon Conversions modified the Mercedes shown here.
I-Spy for 5

The taxi has its origins in the sedan chair, rickshaw, and Hansome cab, Indeed, the licensing authorities still refer to them as 'Hackney carriages'. The vehicles we are concerned with here are the specially built types, and not the private motor cars labelled 'TAXI'.

Traditionally, the Austin Motor Company of Birmingham controlled at least 90 per cent of the taxi market. During the 1960s and '70s, the vehicles were built under licence for them by the BSA motorcycle company. Most recently, they have been built by 'Carbodies'. From time to time, other makes have offered a challenge.

Austin Heavy 12
Based on the 12/4 Austin car chassis powered by a 4-cylinder, 1535 cc engine, this cab was introduced in 1929. The metropolitan authorities insisted on a tighter turning circle in 1930 — a feature still retained on taxis. This example is the classic 'low loader' with worm axle and flat floor.
I-Spy for 25

Austin FX3
Designed from the outset as a taxi, this cab was powered by the Austin Sixteen H.P. 4-cylinder petrol engine. Later models were converted to diesel using the Ferguson tractor engine! All taxis carry a licence plate on the rear. What information is on it?

_____

_____

I-Spy for 20
Double with answer

29

Austin FX4
Initially an Austin and usually BMC 'B' series diesel powered, this taxi has been manufactured by 'Carbodies' (part of the BSA Motorcycle Company) and is now known as the 'Fairway' Bronze or Silver.
I-Spy for 5

Beardmore
This was a valiant attempt to break Austin's monopoly of the cab market. It was powered by a 4-cylinder Ford Consul or 'Perkins 99' diesel. This example is known as the Paramount.
I-Spy for 50

Metrocab
Built by MCW (of bus fame), it borrows heavily from the Ford and Perkins parts bin (Transit axles and gearbox). The body is easily repaired glass fibre.
I-Spy for 10

Winchester Mk III
This was developed by Winchester Autos for Westminster Insurance — who insure London cabs. The body was designed and made in glass fibre by Wincanton Transport. The mechanicals were Ford Cortina based.
I-Spy for 50

Winchester Mk IV
Updated in 1968, using a chassis by Keewest Developments and body by Wincanton, this was the last and most successful Winchester design. Mechanicals are Ford Cortina and some have diesel conversions.
I-Spy for 25

THE COACH AND BODY BUILDERS

See how many of the following makes you can I-Spy. Manufacturers of the bodies are more easily recognized than the chassis underneath!

Alexander 'R'-type
One of Britain's largest independent coachbuilders, Alexander hails from Falkirk in Scotland. Its products can be seen all over the world including China, the Philippines, and Malaysia! The pronounced vee to the upper-deck windows is a styling feature on the 'R'-type double-deck body.
I-Spy for 5

Alexander 'Y'-type
The Alexander 'Y'-type single-deck body has been made in large quantities over many years. It has a timeless elegance.
I-Spy for 15

Bova (Airflow)
In 1982, Bova introduced a streamlined integral coach powered by a rear-mounted DAF diesel. The distinctive chin on the front is an aerodynamic aid to improve fuel consumption. Bova comes from the Netherlands.
I-Spy for 15

Some coaches appear to have two exhaust pipes! The smaller-diameter pipe comes from a diesel-oil-fired heater which circulates hot water or air through the vehicle when heat from the engine coolant is not available during lengthy stopovers.
I-Spy for 10

Bova

Bova has also produced a low-priced integral coach of conventional appearance with a rear-mounted DAF turbo-charged engine.
I-Spy for 10

Caetano

Pioneers of continental coachwork in Britain, Salvador Caetano is a Portuguese manufacturer which is sometimes badged as 'Moseley Continental' by the importing company. Early examples are rather heavily ornamented with chrome grilles and rubbing strips.
I-Spy for 10

Carlyle

Carlyle is the trading name of the former Midland Red Body Works in Birmingham. It is confined to minibus bodies.
I-Spy for 5

Duple Britannia
Duple Bodies has a long history: early types have names like 'Vista', 'Vega', 'Viceroy', 'Viscount' although the example here is a Britannia on an AEC Reliance.
I-Spy for 10

Duple
After mixed fortunes in the 1970s, Duple was taken over by the Hestair Group (which owns Dennis), and modern designs have been badged 'Goldliner', 'Dominant', 'Laser', and 'Caribbean'. This example is on a Dennis chassis.
I-Spy for 5

ECW
Eastern Coach Works (ECW), based in Lowestoft, was firmly established in the 1950s as the principal body builder for the Tilling Group of bus companies. Best known for bus bodies (especially double-deck), they also made coaches. This example is on a Bristol RE.
I-Spy for 15

ECW

During the 1970s and '80s, ECW double-deck bodies on Bristol VR chassis were industry-standard outside London. These buses are still the mainstay of double-deck fleets throughout Britain.

I-Spy for 5

East Lancashire

East Lancashire Coach Builders specialize in building double-deck bodies at their Blackburn factory, and have found favour particularly with south-coast municipal operators. This manufacturer was chosen for design and manufacture of the Olympian-based double-deck coach shown here.

I-Spy for 15

Icarus

Icarus is a new arrival on the British coach scene. Produced in Hungary, they are imported and adapted by Plaxton which completes the trim and markets them.

I-Spy for 15

THE COACH AND BODY BUILDERS

G974LRP

Jonkheere
Jonkheere is another product of the Netherlands, usually imported on Volvo or DAF chassis. Early examples are badged 'Jubilee' or 'Bermuda'. The latest design is the 'Deauville' shown here.
I-Spy for 15

LAG
LAG is a Belgian builder whose products are now seen in Britain, when complete coaches are imported on DAF or Volvo chassis.
I-Spy for 15

Northern Counties

Northern Counties of Wigan is a long-established coachbuilder in double-deck bodywork.
*I-Spy for **10***

Optare

Optare was formed out of the old Roe coachbuilders of Leeds. Noted for futuristic designs, Optare has taken over the design of Metro Rider from MCW. Look out for their striking new full-size city bus single-decker.
*I-Spy for **10***

Park Royal

Park Royal was based in the London suburb of the same name. The company logo is a sedan chair. Park Royal succumbed to a damaging strike and closed down in 1983. Most recently the company produced double-deckers, including early Titans, and the standard design for N.B.C. fleets shown here.
*I-Spy for **10***

Plaxton

Plaxton introduced a new style, known as the Paramount, in 1982. It is available as the 3200 normal height or 3500 high-floor layout. The main distinguishing feature is the short window above the front axle. What symbol does Plaxton Coachwork of Scarborough use as a logo?

I-Spy for 5
Double with answer

Plaxton Double-deck Coach

Responding to a concept that began with Auwater's German Neoplan Skyliner in 1980, Plaxton developed the Paramount 4000 and still produces a luxury double-decker.
I-Spy for 15

Van Hool

Van Hool bodies are made in Belgium and are often married to Volvo Biom chassis. The Alizee is the conventional-height body. The Acron is a high-floor integral with MAN or DAF running units. Which is yours?

I-Spy for 10

Van Hool-McArdle
Van Hool-McArdle is an Irish subsidiary of the Belgian company, set up to make bodies for 'Coras Iompair Eireann' (C.I.E.) the Irish state transport company. These have now been exported.
I-Spy for 15

Willowbrook
Willowbrook, based in Loughborough, was noted for some elegant coach bodies, but most recent production takes the form of angular, functional, single-deck buses. This Crusader body is mounted on a Leopard chassis.
I-Spy for 10

Black and White
Based in Cheltenham and founded in 1926 by Mr George Readings, the company has undergone many changes — it was once part of Midland Red, then Associated Motorways, National Express, and has recently reasserted its independence.
I-Spy for 15

Flights
Flight Tours are based in Birmingham and their flagship operation involves the use of high-specification coaches on interairport shuttle services and London terminuses.
I-Spy for 15

Grey Green
Grey Green is an old, established coaching company founded by George Ewer. The company was bought out by Cowies Motors Group — importers of DAF vehicles.
I-Spy for 15

National Express
National Express is the coaching operation left over from N.B.C. At various times, it absorbed many famous names, including Black and White, Royal Blue, Ribble, Midland Red, and more.
I-Spy for 10

Shearings
Shearings are an excursion and package holiday operator of national repute based in Wigan.
I-Spy for 10

Wallace Arnold
Wallace Arnold are almost an institution and have promoted coaching
holidays for many years.
I-Spy for **15**

Foreign Coaches
Touring holidays
and school
exchange visits
have resulted in
increasing numbers
of foreign coaches
on the roads of
Britain. This
Setra is
French.
I-Spy for **15**

Articulated Bus

Articulated buses were banned in Britain until 1977 when trials took place in Sheffield. Their use on fare-paying services was not authorized until 1980. Although popular in Europe, Britain prefers double-deckers for high-capacity buses, and airports are the best place to see 'bendy-buses'!
I-Spy for 25

Overall Advert Bus

London Transport was the first operator to exploit this money-making idea in 1969 (on a Routemaster for Silexene paint!). Overall advert buses are now quite common and colourful.
I-Spy for 10

Open-top Bus

Popular at the seaside and at tourist attractions, these vehicles are often cut-down older buses suited to less rigorous summer season use. This example is an early 27-foot Bristol Lowdekka.
I-Spy for 10

School Bus

Not many are as smart and colourful as this one! Based on a Bedford YMP low-profile chassis, the Wadham Stringer body incorporates tail-lift entrance for children in wheelchairs.
I-Spy for 10

Trolley Bus

The last trolley buses ran in Bradford in 1972. Picking up electric current from overhead wires, these quiet, pollution-free vehicles suffered from high initial system cost and lack of operating flexibility. The National Museum at Sandtoft, Doncaster and the Black Country Museum, Dudley still run them.
I-Spy for 50

Tram

A common sight on city streets a century ago, trams can only be seen on active service at two seaside locations and in museums (The National Tram Museum, Crich in Derbyshire and Dudley's Black Country Museum have the largest collections).

Single-deck Tram
I-Spy for 25

Double-deck Tram
I-Spy for 25

45

The Scrapyard

Because they are large and tough, buses linger for a long time. They make useful covered storage and many 'sheds' have been rescued and restored. Skilful recognition would identify this as an AEC.

I-Spy for 10

Mobile Exhibition Unit

Modified with a generator and display lighting, old buses make excellent hospitality suites at exhibitions and shows.

I-Spy for 15

A Home

Old coaches can be used as mobile or static homes. Many interesting vehicles are used by 'the new age travellers'. This old AEC is obviously well cared for.

I-Spy for 10

Recovery Vehicle

Bus companies can save the cost of a purpose-built breakdown crane by cutting down an old bus. The Leyland PD2 shown here is being painted after some drastic surgery.
I-Spy for 20

Playbus

Another use for out-of-service vehicles. Brightly coloured, fitted with heaters, water, and even sandpits, they can be driven to areas of town where the children lack good play areas.
I-Spy for 15

Roadside Café

Bus operators were quick to use old buses as crew canteens. Private enterprise has adopted the idea for the roadside lay-by.
I-Spy for 15

INDEX

Answers

AEC Routemaster: Associated Equipment Company. AEC Regent: Public Carrying Vehicle. Bedford: Luton, Bedfordshire. Leyland: Seddon Atkinson. Mercedes-Benz: a circle enclosing a three-pointed star. Austin FX3: seating capacity and town/county of origin. Plaxton: a stylized castle representing the one at Scarborough.

© I-Spy Limited 1992

ISBN (paperback) 1 85671 112 9

Michelin Tyre Public Limited Company
Davy House, Lyon Road, Harrow, Middlesex HA1 2DQ

MICHELIN and the Michelin Man are Registered Trademarks of Michelin

All rights reserved. No part of this publication may be reproduced, stored in a retrieval system, or transmitted in any form or by any means, electronic, mechanical photocopying or otherwise without the prior written permission of I-Spy Limited.

A CIP record for this title is available from the British Library.

Edited and designed by Curtis Garratt Limited, The Old Vicarage, Horton cum Studley, Oxford OX9 1BT

The Publisher gratefully acknowledges the contribution of the Oxford Bus Museum Trust and Alex Ayres who provided the majority of the photographs in this I-Spy book. Additional photographs by Sotheby's and Peter Greenland Photography. The Publisher also wishes to acknowledge Alex Ayres who wrote the text.

Colour reproduction by Norwich Litho Services Limited.

Printed in Spain.